THE TRANSFORMERS

MORE THAN MEETS THE EYE!

AUTOBOT

DECEPTICON

This book belongs to ....

THE TRANSFORMERS™ ANNUAL published by MARVEL COMICS LTD., 23 Redan Place, London W2 4SA, in association with GRANDREAMS LTD., Jadwin House, 205-211 Kentish Town Road, London NW5.

£3.25

I am the mighty MEGATRON, leader of the Decepticons, cunning and ruthless! I shall not rest until I have conquered the Autobots and rule Earth and Cybertron!

I am STARSCREAM, Decepticon Air Commander! I am the fastest flier and the most handsome of the Decepticons – and I believe I would be the best ruler!

I am RAVAGE, Decepticon saboteur. I am crafty and aloof and can virtually escape detection as I carry out my deadly strategies!

I am SKYWARP and I love to attack the Autobots! I also like to play cruel pranks on my fellow Decepticons. . .

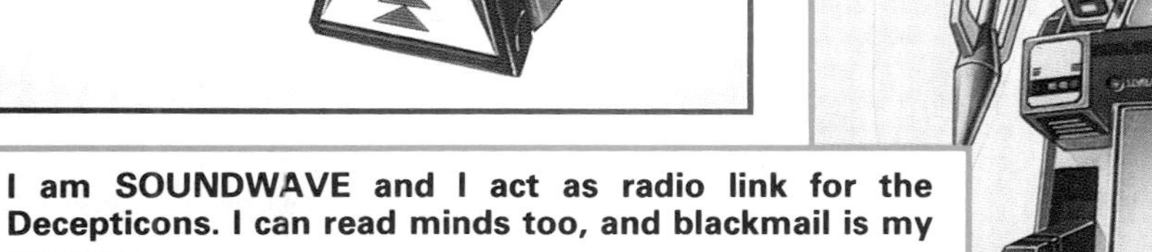

I am SOUNDWAVE and I act as radio link for the Decepticons. I can read minds too, and blackmail is my weapon. . .

I am RUMBLE, quick-tempered and mean – and I can shatter the ground with low frequency groundwaves.

I am LASERBEAK and my prey is enemy battle survivors! My function is to interrogate the enemy and I do this with my laser cannons.

MARVEL

TRANSFORMERS

HEROIC AUTOBOT

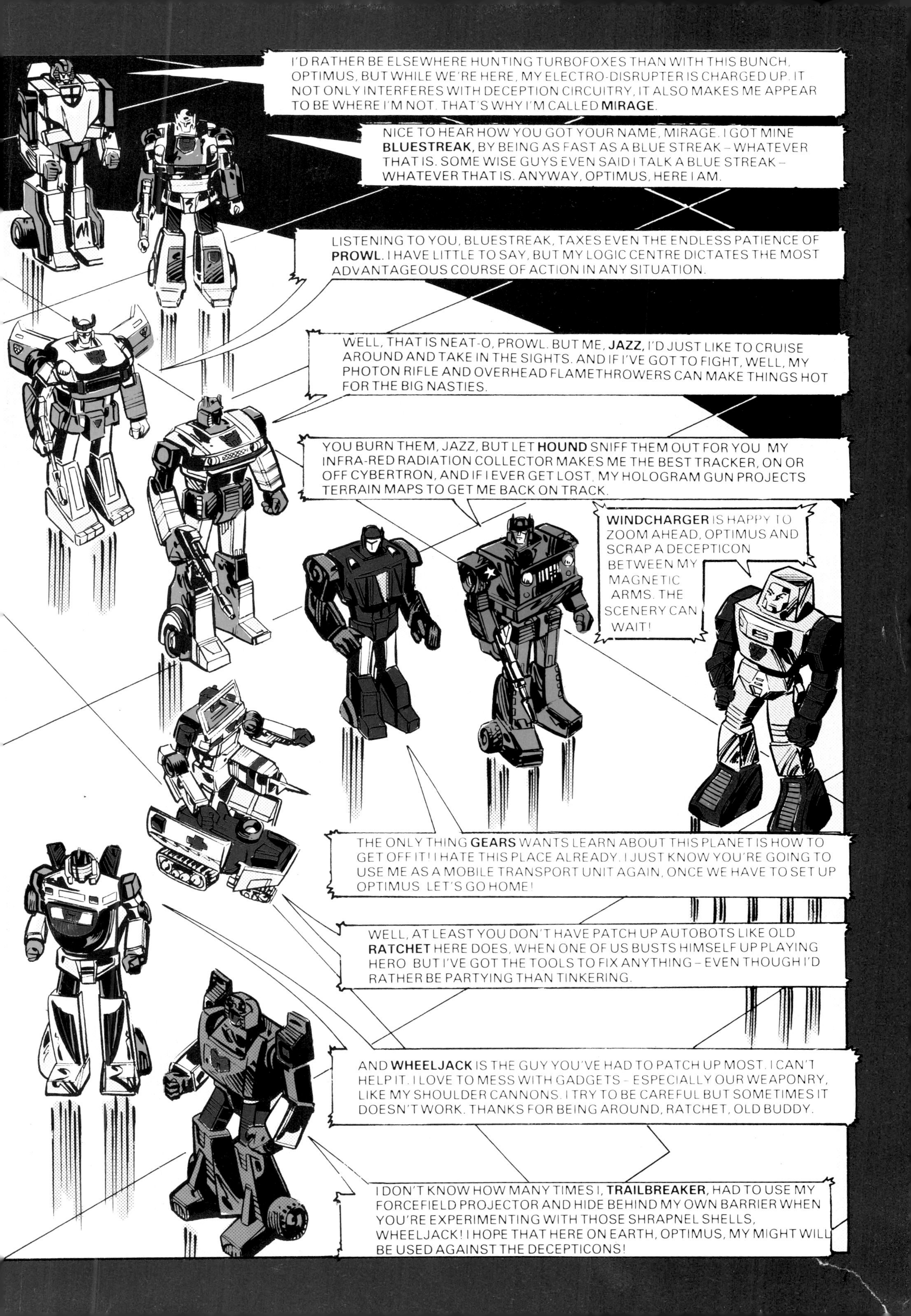
I'D RATHER BE ELSEWHERE HUNTING TURBOFOXES THAN WITH THIS BUNCH, OPTIMUS, BUT WHILE WE'RE HERE, MY ELECTRO-DISRUPTER IS CHARGED UP. IT NOT ONLY INTERFERES WITH DECEPTION CIRCUITRY, IT ALSO MAKES ME APPEAR TO BE WHERE I'M NOT. THAT'S WHY I'M CALLED MIRAGE.
NICE TO HEAR HOW YOU GOT YOUR NAME, MIRAGE. I GOT MINE BLUESTREAK, BY BEING AS FAST AS A BLUE STREAK – WHATEVER THAT IS. SOME WISE GUYS EVEN SAID I TALK A BLUE STREAK – WHATEVER THAT IS. ANYWAY, OPTIMUS, HERE I AM.
LISTENING TO YOU, BLUESTREAK, TAXES EVEN THE ENDLESS PATIENCE OF PROWL. I HAVE LITTLE TO SAY, BUT MY LOGIC CENTRE DICTATES THE MOST ADVANTAGEOUS COURSE OF ACTION IN ANY SITUATION.
WELL, THAT IS NEAT-O, PROWL. BUT ME, JAZZ, I'D JUST LIKE TO CRUISE AROUND AND TAKE IN THE SIGHTS. AND IF I'VE GOT TO FIGHT, WELL, MY PHOTON RIFLE AND OVERHEAD FLAMETHROWERS CAN MAKE THINGS HOT FOR THE BIG NASTIES.
YOU BURN THEM, JAZZ, BUT LET HOUND SNIFF THEM OUT FOR YOU. MY INFRA-RED RADIATION COLLECTOR MAKES ME THE BEST TRACKER, ON OR OFF CYBERTRON, AND IF I EVER GET LOST, MY HOLOGRAM GUN PROJECTS TERRAIN MAPS TO GET ME BACK ON TRACK.
WINDCHARGER IS HAPPY TO ZOOM AHEAD, OPTIMUS AND SCRAP A DECEPTICON BETWEEN MY MAGNETIC ARMS. THE SCENERY CAN WAIT!
THE ONLY THING GEARS WANTS LEARN ABOUT THIS PLANET IS HOW TO GET OFF IT! I HATE THIS PLACE ALREADY. I JUST KNOW YOU'RE GOING TO USE ME AS A MOBILE TRANSPORT UNIT AGAIN, ONCE WE HAVE TO SET UP OPTIMUS. LET'S GO HOME!
WELL, AT LEAST YOU DON'T HAVE PATCH UP AUTOBOTS LIKE OLD RATCHET HERE DOES, WHEN ONE OF US BUSTS HIMSELF UP PLAYING HERO. BUT I'VE GOT THE TOOLS TO FIX ANYTHING – EVEN THOUGH I'D RATHER BE PARTYING THAN TINKERING.
AND WHEELJACK IS THE GUY YOU'VE HAD TO PATCH UP MOST. I CAN'T HELP IT. I LOVE TO MESS WITH GADGETS – ESPECIALLY OUR WEAPONRY, LIKE MY SHOULDER CANNONS. I TRY TO BE CAREFUL BUT SOMETIMES IT DOESN'T WORK. THANKS FOR BEING AROUND, RATCHET, OLD BUDDY.
I DON'T KNOW HOW MANY TIMES I, TRAILBREAKER, HAD TO USE MY FORCEFIELD PROJECTOR AND HIDE BEHIND MY OWN BARRIER WHEN YOU'RE EXPERIMENTING WITH THOSE SHRAPNEL SHELLS, WHEELJACK! I HOPE THAT HERE ON EARTH, OPTIMUS, MY MIGHT WILL BE USED AGAINST THE DECEPTICONS!

WASHINGTON D.C.
THEY ARE COMING!

THE WORD HAS SPREAD THROUGH THE CITY LIKE WILDFIRE... THEY HAVE BEEN SIGHTED!
THEY ARE NO CONVENTIONAL ENEMY...

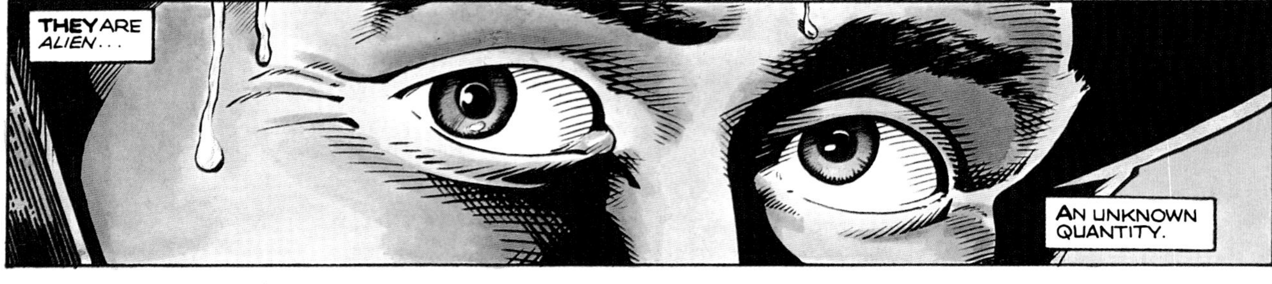
THEY ARE ALIEN...
AN UNKNOWN QUANTITY.

STORIES, RUMOURS, HAVE CIRCULATED... BUT NO-ONE TRULY KNOWS WHAT TO EXPECT...
CERTAINLY NOTHING AS MUNDANE AS AN ARTICULATED LORRY, A PATROL CAR AND A TANK!
THE AUTOBOTS HAVE COME TO TOWN..!

HOLD YOUR FIRE UNLESS I GIVE THE ORDER, MEN - LET'S JUST LEAD THEM RIGHT ONTO...

"THE LAWN OF THE WHITE HOUSE ITSELF!"
AND FROM THAT BUILDING STRIDES A MAN WHO WILL ATTEMPT TO MAKE PEACE WITH THESE BEINGS WHO HAVE INVADED NOT ONLY THIS COUNTRY... BUT ALSO THIS PLANET!
A MAN WHO THIS DAY MUST LEARN TO CO-EXIST WITH ALIEN BEINGS.
I WELCOME YOU WITH THE OPEN HAND OF PEACE AND FRIENDSHIP...
IN THE NAME OF THE AMERICAN PEOPLE I GREET YOU... THE AUTOBOTS!
HOWEVER, I FIND THE PROSPECT OF HOLDING A CONVERSATION WITH A LORRY A LITTLE DISCONCERTING!

SCRIPT: FURMAN ART: COLLINS/ANDERSON LETTERS: STARKINGS COLOURS: HART EDITOR: CRANNA

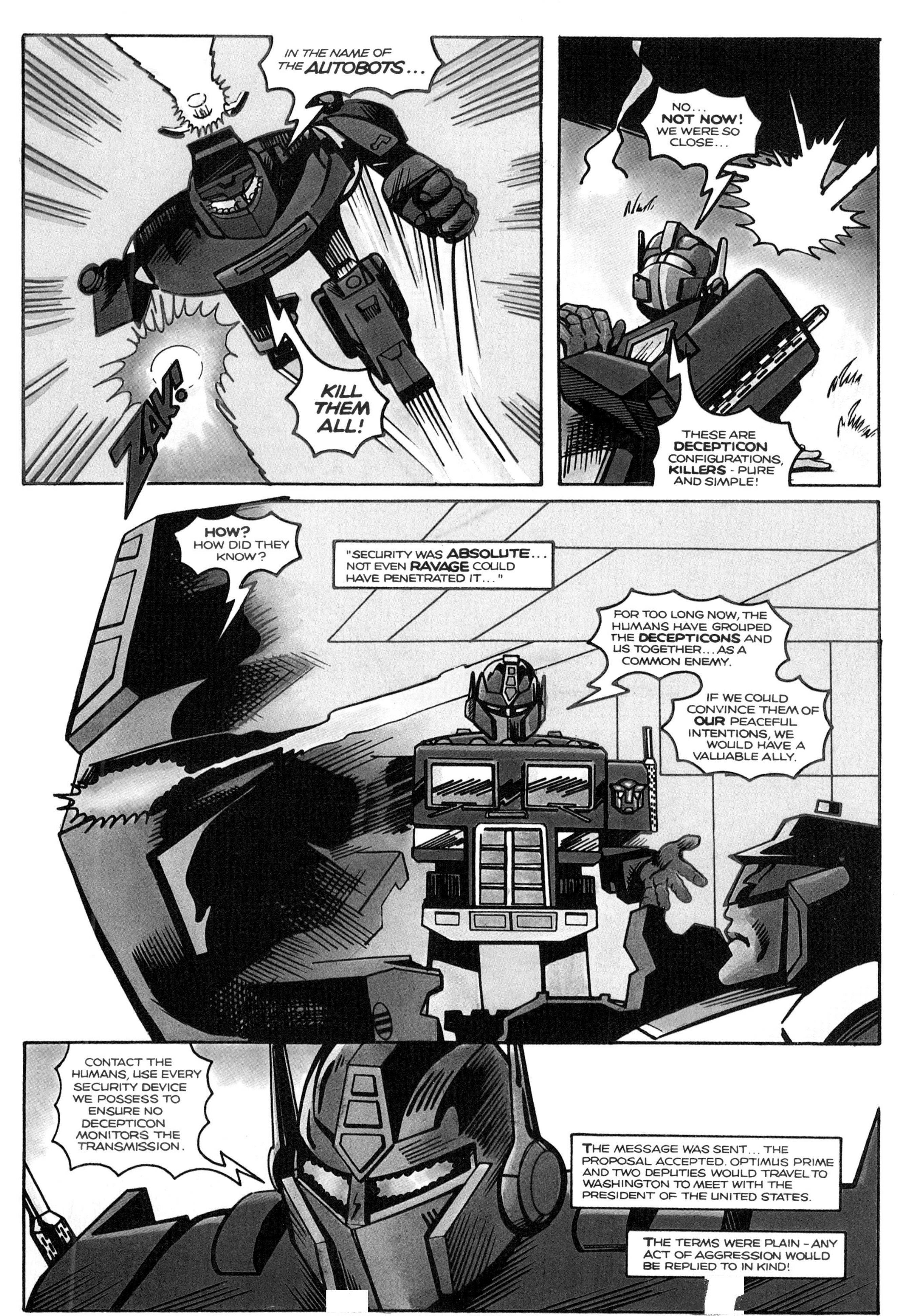
IN THE NAME OF THE AUTOBOTS...
KILL THEM ALL!
ZAK!
NO... NOT NOW! WE WERE SO CLOSE...
THESE ARE DECEPTICON CONFIGURATIONS, KILLERS - PURE AND SIMPLE!
HOW? HOW DID THEY KNOW?
"SECURITY WAS ABSOLUTE... NOT EVEN RAVAGE COULD HAVE PENETRATED IT..."
FOR TOO LONG NOW, THE HUMANS HAVE GROUPED THE DECEPTICONS AND US TOGETHER... AS A COMMON ENEMY.
IF WE COULD CONVINCE THEM OF OUR PEACEFUL INTENTIONS, WE WOULD HAVE A VALUABLE ALLY.
CONTACT THE HUMANS, USE EVERY SECURITY DEVICE WE POSSESS TO ENSURE NO DECEPTICON MONITORS THE TRANSMISSION.
THE MESSAGE WAS SENT... THE PROPOSAL ACCEPTED. OPTIMUS PRIME AND TWO DEPUTIES WOULD TRAVEL TO WASHINGTON TO MEET WITH THE PRESIDENT OF THE UNITED STATES.
THE TERMS WERE PLAIN - ANY ACT OF AGGRESSION WOULD BE REPLIED TO IN KIND!

IT SHOULD HAVE BEEN FOOLPROOF – ALL DETAILS AND ARRANGEMENTS WERE MADE UNDER STRICT SECURITY...
EXCEPT ONE! ONE CARELESS CALL WITHOUT SCRAMBLER PROCEDURES... ONE MISTAKE!
AND SOMETIMES ONE IS ALL IT TAKES...
UNBELIEVABLE! HOW HAVE I FAILED TO MONITOR THIS BEFORE? MEGATRON MUST BE INFORMED..!
MEGATRON – LEADER OF THE EVIL DECEPTICONS!
YOU HAVE DONE WELL, SOUNDWAVE. YOUR CEASELESS MONITORING OF THIS PLANET'S AIRWAVES HAS BORNE FRUIT!
A TREATY BETWEEN THE HUMANS AND THE AUTOBOTS MUST NOT COME TO PASS!
BUT STEALTH AND CUNNING ARE CALLED FOR... AN OPEN ATTACK BY US WOULD MERELY UNDERLINE THE AUTOBOTS' CLAIMS...
NO, WE MUST INTRODUCE A TROOP OF DECEPTICONS TO THE MEETING SITE BY STEALTH...
I THINK IT IS TIME TO AWAKEN... THE INSECTICONS!

WASHINGTON D.C.–THE INSECTICON SHRAPNEL PREPARES FOR ANOTHER MURDEROUS ASSAULT...
ALL ENEMIES OF THE AUTOBOTS MUST DIE!
HOWEVER THEY CAME TO BE HERE, THEIR THREAT IS EVIDENT...
PROWL, WARPATH – PICK YOUR TARGETS CAREFULLY...WE MUST AVOID HITTING THE HUMANS!
SHRACK!
AND, ALTHOUGH THE INSECTICONS DODGE THE HAIL OF LASER FIRE, IT DOES NOT ESCAPE OPTIMUS PRIME'S NOTICE THAT THEIR MOVEMENTS ARE SOMEWHAT UNCERTAIN...

THEN, SUDDENLY, BOMBSHELL BREAKS OFF HIS ATTACK...

THE TRANSFORMERS NAME AND FACE MATCH!

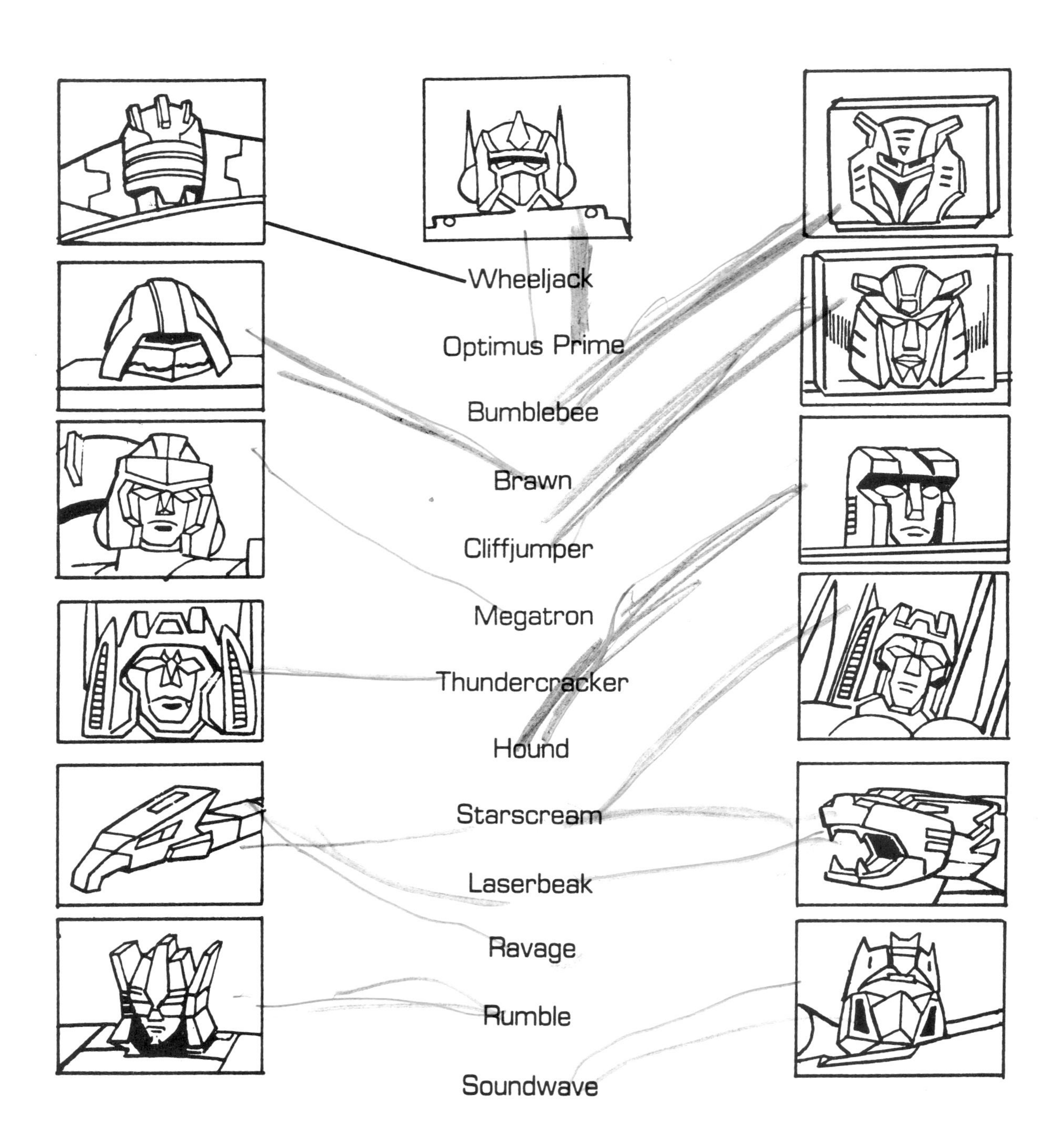

The solution to this puzzle is on page 62.

Match the name and face! We did the first one to show you how!

AND ANNOUNCES TO THE STUNNED AUTOBOTS...
GREAT OPTIMUS, WE HEAR YOUR COMMAND. WE WILL TAKE THE BATTLE TO THE CITY ITSELF, LEAVING YOU TO FINISH OFF THE SOLDIERS...

DID YOU HEAR THAT?
DID YOU HEAR WHAT THAT THING SAID?!
I HEARD.
OBVIOUSLY THEIR TARGET FOR DESTRUCTION IS NOT US BUT OUR NAME!
UH, I HATE TO INTERRUPT THESE DELIBERATIONS...
"BUT I THINK THEY'VE SUCEEDED..."
YOU MURDERING MONSTROSITIES! IF WE HADN'T MANAGED TO GET THE PRESIDENT TO SAFETY, YOU'D HAVE HIS DEATH TO ANSWER FOR...
AS IT IS, I'M SIMPLY GONNA BLOW YOU BACK TO WHATEVER PLANET YOU CAME FROM FOR ALL THE DESTRUCTION YOU'VE CAUSED...

SPLIT UP, PROWL, WARPATH - YOU'LL HAVE TO DEAL WITH THE INSECTICONS WITHOUT MY HELP!

BECAUSE IF WHAT I BELIEVE IS TRUE, I MAY BE ABLE TO TO *DESTROY* THESE INSECTICONS AT **SOURCE!**

QUICKLY OUTDISTANCING THE TROOPS, THE TWO VALIANT AUTOBOTS *MADE* THEIR WAY INTO DOWNTOWN WASHINGTON.
WEOOOO
WEOOO
POLICE

WHAT DO YOU RECKON OPTIMUS IS UP TO..?
I WOULDN'T WASTE TIME TRYING TO FIGURE THAT ONE OUT...
WEO WEO WEO WEO

AS THEY ROUND THE NEXT CORNER, PROWL AND WARPATH ARE CONFRONTED...
WE'VE GOT A JOB TO DO...
SO LET'S GET...
POLICE

...WITH A SCENE OF
HORROR AND DESTRUCTION!
RIMMER'S OOPTICIAN
FURMAN'S WEIGHT WATCHERS
ON... WITH... IT...

CONTINUED ON PAGE 51

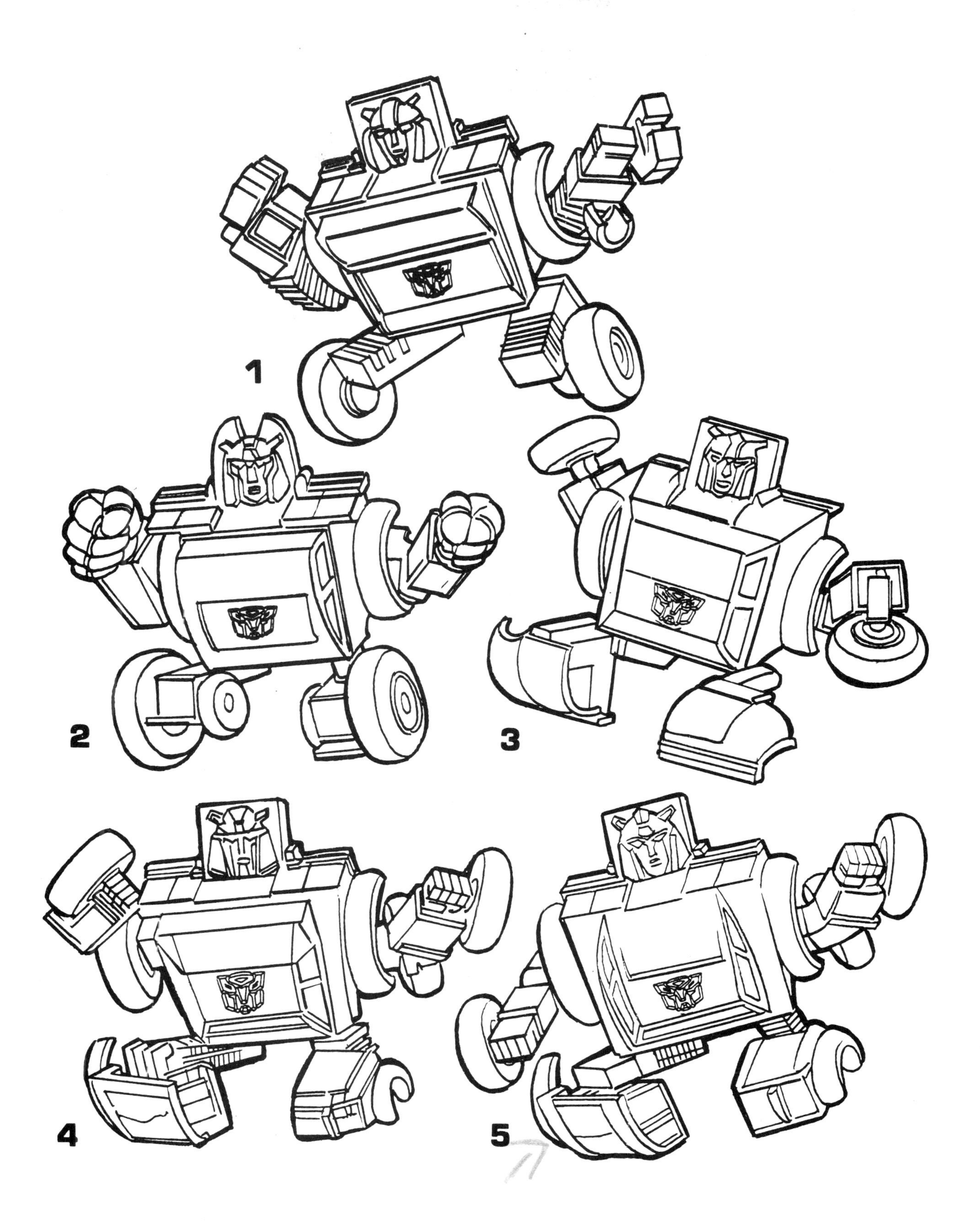

Find the exact outline of the fastest Autobot—Cliffjumper.

The solution to this puzzle is on page 62.

MISSING IN ACTION

For Tracks, it had been a simple reconnaissance mission. Until he ran into Rumble...

Despite its name, Greater Portland is a small town. Its population never exceeds ten thousand and everyone seems to know each other's business... not that they'd admit it. It's a quiet and peaceful town; at least it was, before the aliens arrived.

"AAARRGH!" The Autobot Tracks stumbled and fell into the grime of the alley. His robotic body showed the scars of combat. The mission he had thought would be a simple one had gone horribly wrong, for instead of being able to confirm the absence of Decepticon activity in the area, he had been set upon by the evil Rumble in a surprise attack!

He looked up now at the menacing form of the Decepticon. Rumble, whose power to create earth tremors had thrown the Autobot off balance, so that now he lay at the Decepticon's mercy! There was a ruthless grin on Rumble's face.

"I have you now!" he said.

Tracks reached instinctively for his black beam gun. Quickly, he raised the weapon and fired a ray of black light at his enemy. Rumble was suddenly cloaked in blinding darkness. Tracks began to raise himself, his confidence quickly returning.

"That's what you think!" he said, smiling.

Without warning, Rumble's arm thrust out of the darkness and into the Autobot's chest cavity. Tracks was convulsed with incredible pain. His sensors began to malfunction, as Rumble ripped and tore at his vital micro-circuitry. It seemed like forever before he was released from the tortuous grasp.

Tracks fell back onto the ground. The pain persisted and he knew he was about to become non-functional...

"You always were over-confident," Rumble sneered. "Now it's too late to do anything about it. You're finished! That's one fewer of your kind to stand in the way of the rule of the Decepticons!"

With that, Rumble turned and strode off, leaving Tracks for dead in the alleyway. He reflected on the lucky chance that had led him to come across Tracks in the town. But now he must continue with the mission he had been sent on by Megatron, before he could return with the news of his victory...

In a final effort to avoid unconsciousness, Tracks transformed into his vehicle mode, a Corvette Stingray. But the action used up the last of his energy and the Autobot remained motionless, stranded far from his fellow Autobots in the dark, concealing alley.

WHERE'S TRACKS?

"I'm afraid we can wait no longer," Optimus Prime told the gathered Autobots. A council of war had been called, which Tracks had been expected to address. However he had failed to return from his reconnaissance mission to Greater Portland and Optimus Prime was becoming increasingly worried.

"Perhaps he's come into conflict with the Decepticons," said Brawn, voicing his leader's concern.

"I doubt it," Mirage interrupted. "That Earth-lover is probably wasting time driving around Greater Portland's streets, exploring the town and showing himself off." There was a murmur of agreement.

Optimus Prime was not convinced. He knew of Tracks' vain streak, but he was sure that the Autobot would never miss such an important meeting on purpose. "Enough!" he cried and the Autobots fell silent. "Jazz, I want you to travel to Greater Portland and investigate."

"Certainly," said the warrior Autobot, as he stood up to leave the Ark's council room.

FOUND!

J.D. entered the alley and stared at the Corvette Stingray parked amongst the old rubbish bags and discarded beer cans. There was a faint whimpering coming from the vehicle and the youth thought at first that someone had not only abandoned their car but their child as well. As J.D. began to walk up the alley toward the car, the whimpering seemed to grow louder.

Warily, he stretched an arm out and touched the Corvette's door. The whimpering stopped and the door miraculously sprung open. The car was empty. He must have been mistaken about the whimpering, he decided.

Mark Brookes sat on the kerb outside Lou's Bar. J.D. was late. But J.D. had never been late, not in all the years that the two had known each other. *He's lost his nerve,* thought Mark, *after all the planning, he's lost his nerve!* Mark stood up, not sure whether he was disappointed. It had been months before when J.D. and first, half-jokingly, suggested that the two perform a robbery... a simple hold-up, using the gun that Mark's father kept hidden in his desk's top drawer. In the time tht had followed, Mark and J.D. had finalised their plans. Mark would steal the gun, while J.D. would provide a suitable get-away car. They would then meet at Lou's bar. All had gone perfectly, except now J.D. was late.

"Hey, Mark!"

Mark spun around in the direction from which he heard J.D.'s voice. His friend was drawing up to the kerb behind the wheel of a rather battered Corvette.

J.D. switched off the ignition.

"Where did you get it?" Mark asked, amazed.

"Would you believe I found it in the alley behind Woolworth's!"

"Aw c'mon J.D., stop foolin'," Mark laughed. He opened the passenger door. "Let's go, before the store closes!"

From the doorway of his bar, Lou watched the pair drive off with a slow shake of his head.

Those two would come to a bad end, he was sure of it. Young Mark wasn't such a tearaway, but he'd got himself into real bad company with that J.D. And goodness only knew where they'd got that car from...

He turned and went back inside. There was nothing worse than boredom for getting kids into trouble and he was willing to wager that with those two, it would be Trouble with a capital T.

ON THE TRAIL

Mark sat nervously behind the wheel of the Corvette. The car was parked outside the supermarket they'd selected and J.D., the small pistol tucked into the pocket of his coat had entered the store ten minutes ago. *What's keeping him?* Mark thought frantically. All he had to do was force the cashier to give him the money from the checkout.

Suddenly there was a crack of gunfire and J.D. bolted out of the store's doorway. "Drive!" he yelled at Mark, as he scrambled into the Corvette's passenger seat.

"What happened?" Mark asked.

"One of the cashiers," gasped J.D., "she pressed an alarm button."

"But I heard a gunshot!"

"I was waving the gun and it accidentally fired. No-one was injured," J.D. said, an expression of relief on his face. "Let's get out of here before the cops arrive!"

Mark started the car's engine and pulled away from the kerb. "Where to, then?" he asked.

"East," replied J.D. determinedly. "We're going to New York!"

VITAL CLUE

A week after J.D. and Mark's failed robbery attempt, Optimus Prime sat alone. A large cable connected his chest cavity to the Ark's main computer terminal and energy flowed from the spacecraft into his massive form. The search for Tracks had proved fruitless and although Optimus had ordered more Autobots to begin looking for their missing companion, he did not expect success. Suddenly he was broken out of his thoughts by the diminutive form of Cosmos.

"Optimus Prime!" cried the communications Autobot, as he barged into the chamber.

"Yes, Cosmos?" Optimus asked, the strain of the last week showing slightly on his robotic features.

"I've been monitoring the humans' law enforcement computers," replied Cosmos excitedly. "There have been a number of robberies committed recently in the city known as New York. The description of the youths involved matches that of two young men who are wanted in connection with a hold-up in Greater Portland. The get-away car they are using is a Corvette Stingray – and it bears more than a passing resemblance to Tracks!"

Optimus Prime rose from his command chair, disconnecting the cable from his chest. He walked toward the communications Autobot. "Quickly, Cosmos, find Inferno and tell him to report to me immediately."

Shortly after, Inferno was standing in front of his leader.

"It appears two humans have taken Tracks to New York," Optimus said, "I want you to take charge of Grapple and Hoist and travel east to recover him."

SPECIAL SIGN

It was eleven o' clock at night in New York city and ten-year-old Danny Phillips had been in bed for the past two hours. Not that he was asleep; instead, he was flipping through his most prized possession... his scrap book. As the young boy carefully turned the pages, he focused his attention on various newspaper clippings. The clippings were neatly filed away under a variety of headings; the space shuttle and U.F.O. being the largest categories.

Danny came to the last pages of his album. There, carefully pasted down, was an article he'd cut out of last week's newspaper. It was an investigative report on the supposed sightings of extraterrestrial robots in the state of Oregon. Danny began to read the article, for what must have been the fourth time that day. But before he reached the part about the robots attacking each other, he heard his mother walking up the stairs.

Jennifer Phillips was a widow and had been since Danny was four years old. Her husband had died in an accident, while testing an experimental rocket ship for N.A.S.A. He had been a good man, if a little careless, and Jennifer was convinced that his reckless thirst for adventure had contributed to his death. Danny was much like his father, Jennifer had discovered early on, and she soon put a stop to the endless collection of comic books, model spacecraft and astronomy magazines. She would try to keep his feet on the ground.

As his mother entered his room, Danny hid the scrap book under his bed and pretended to be asleep. Jennifer slowly crept toward her son, she gently kissed him on the cheek and turned out the light.

The following day, Danny had agreed to perform some errands for his mother and as he walked down the street, he saw a bright blue Corvette Stingray park outside the bank. Danny was speechless. Despite the countless dents and scratches, the car sparkled in the early morning sunlight. Two men left the vehicle and entered the bank, as Danny crossed the road.

He placed his hand on a large emblem that decorated the car's bonnet. He recognised the strange design, he was sure of it, but where from he couldn't quite remember. Then it came to him... he had seen similar insignia in a photograph that accompanied the latest article he had clipped from the newspaper. The design had been on the bodies of a number of the giant robots.

HOLD-UP!

Excitement swelled within the young boy and he hurried into the bank to talk to the owners of the car. Danny stopped dead. Lined up against the bank's far wall were a number of people, their arms raised in the air and their backs toward a young man, who was holding a

Continued on page 30

Because many of the Decepticons can fly, they are able to cover greater distances in shorter time than the Autobots can. But this advantage has one serious flaw. Unscramble the words in the boxes below and find out what that flaw is.

HEYT	LKYCUIQ
RBNU	PU
ERITH	EUFL.

Answer: They Quickly Burn Up Their Fuel

DECEPTICON MATCH-UP!

Draw a line connecting the Decepticon face with his weapon identity. Look close at the jet planes — they are not all the same! We did the first match-up to show you how.

The solution to this puzzle is on page 62.

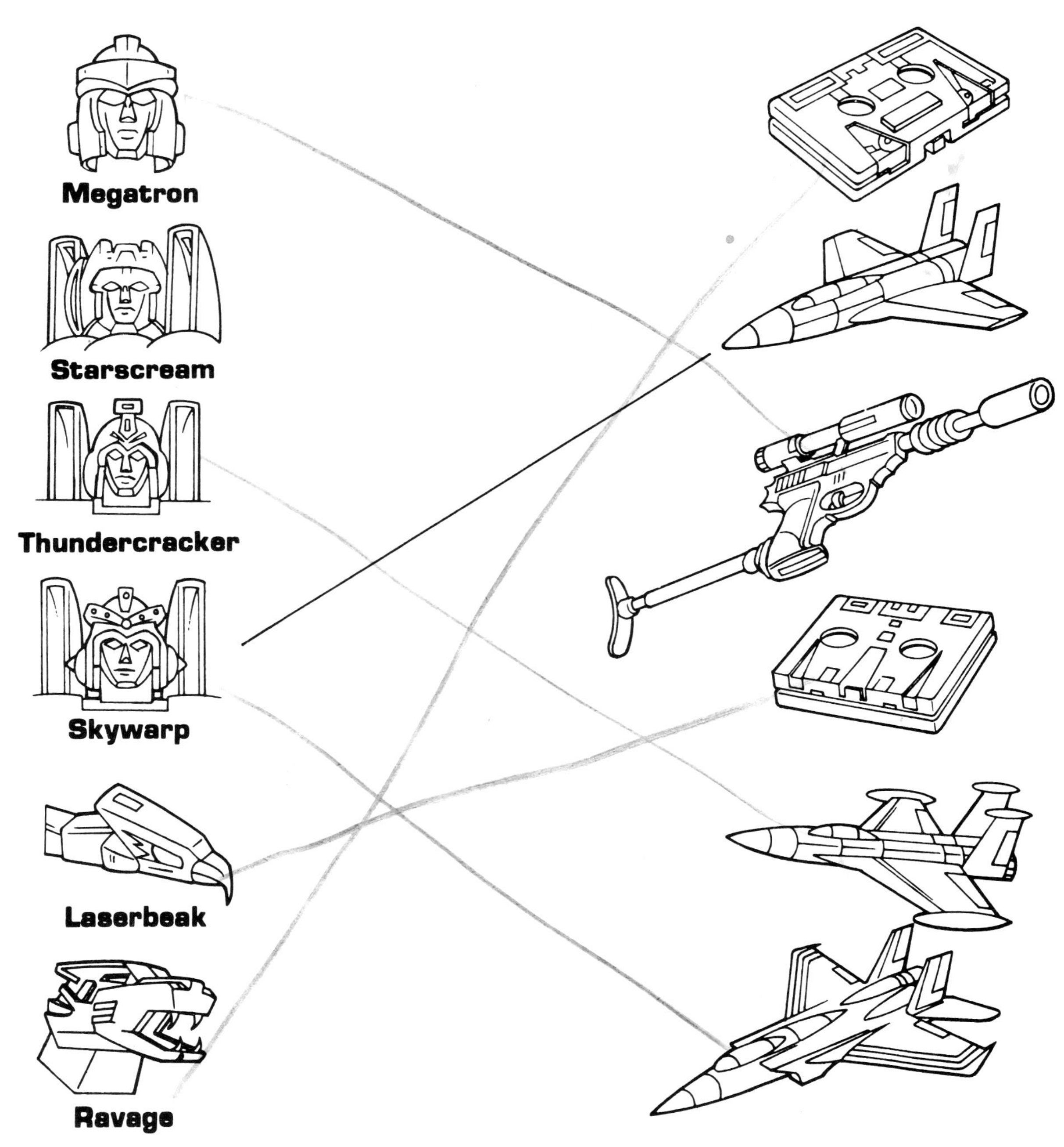

HIGH COUNCILLOR TRAACHON, I BESEECH YOU, USE YOUR RIGHT OF VETO ... FREE THE AUTOBOTS TO FIGHT AS SOLDIERS, NOT POLITICIANS.
DO YOU KNOW OF ONE WHO COULD SHOULDER SUCH RESPONSIBILITY?
YES. YES I DO. HE IS A NATURAL LEADER. HIS NAME IS ...
OPTIMUS PRIME.
AND THERE SHALL COME... A LEADER!
STRIKE FORCE ALPHA, HOLD YOUR GROUND... HOUND, PULSAR, YOU'RE SUPPOSED TO BE GIVING THE GUNNERS COVERING FIRE...
TEMPEST - SEE TO THE SURVIVORS OF GAMMA SQUAD, MAKE SURE THEY'RE TAKEN TO RATCHET...
SCRIPT: SIMON FURMAN
ART: JOHN STOKES
LETTERS: STARKINGS
COLOURS: GINA HART
EDITOR: SHEILA CRANNA

TALES OF CYBERTRON

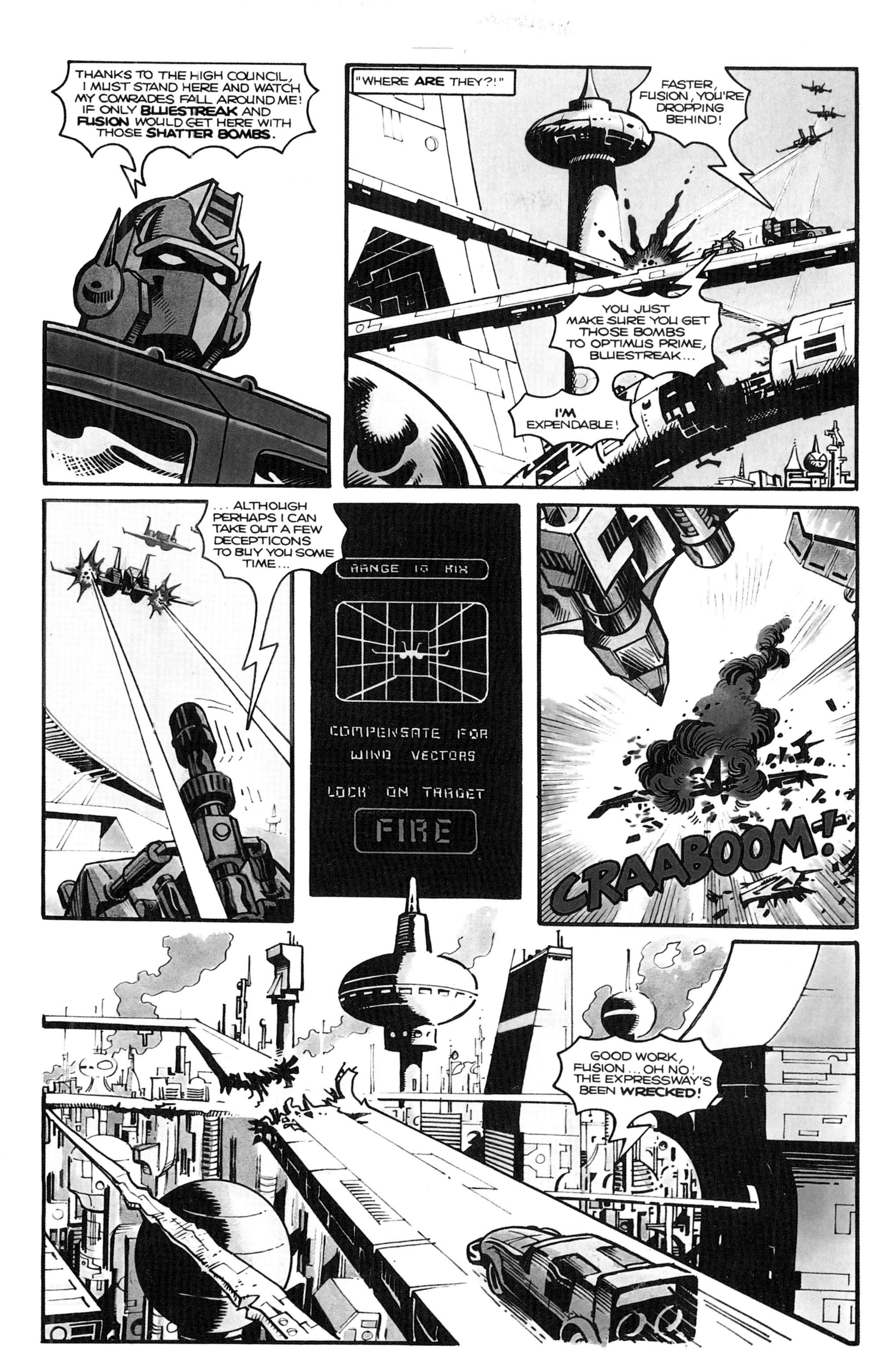

THANKS TO THE HIGH COUNCIL, I MUST STAND HERE AND WATCH MY COMRADES FALL AROUND ME! IF ONLY BLUESTREAK AND FUSION WOULD GET HERE WITH THOSE SHATTER BOMBS.
"WHERE ARE THEY?!"
FASTER, FUSION, YOU'RE DROPPING BEHIND!
YOU JUST MAKE SURE YOU GET THOSE BOMBS TO OPTIMUS PRIME, BLUESTREAK...
I'M EXPENDABLE!
...ALTHOUGH PERHAPS I CAN TAKE OUT A FEW DECEPTICONS TO BUY YOU SOME TIME...
RANGE 10 MIX
COMPENSATE FOR WIND VECTORS
LOCK ON TARGET
FIRE
CRAABOOM!
GOOD WORK, FUSION... OH NO! THE EXPRESSWAY'S BEEN WRECKED!

CONTINUED...

Continued from page **24**

small pistol. Danny recognised him as the driver of the Corvette. Standing in front of the cashier's window, Danny could see the car's other occupant. He was holding a shotgun.

"Oh," whispered the boy.

"What the..." J.D. span around and pointed his weapon at Danny. Suddenly, an alarm bell sounded throughout the bank.

"I told you not to press that button!" J.D. shouted at the cashier. "Now come out from behind there, with your arms in the air! Take the boy and join the others."

"So what do we do now?" asked Mark, as he approached J.D." This place is gonna be swarming with cops soon. They'll storm the building!"

"Not if they know we've got hostages," replied J.D. coolly, "And especially not if they know we've got this." J.D. rummaged about in the small bag he had been carrying with him. Out of it he produced six sticks of dynamite. Attached to the explosives was a small time piece.

"J.D.!" Mark exclaimed. "That's a bomb – are you crazy?"

Several miles away, a driverless fire truck was parked outside an electrical store. At the bottom of the street, a towtruck and a construction truck turned the corner and approached the fire engine... they, too, were empty.

"We managed to tap into the police frequencies, Inferno," the towtruck said, to the alarm of the surrounding shoppers!

"Hoist's right," interrupted the construction vehicle. "The two humans are now inside a bank not far from here. They're surrounded by the law enforcement agencies."

"And Tracks?" Inferno asked.

"He's stationed outside the bank," Grapple continued.

"Well, we'd best get over there and retrieve him!" With this Inferno and his fellow Autobots pulled out from the kerb and drove away.

The Autobots approached the bank. The area surrounding the building had been roped off and a number of uniformed men had been deployed in the immediate vicinity. A handful of police negotiators were standing about, holding loud hailers and photographers and newsmen were already arriving in force.

"There's Tracks," Grapple cried, motioning to the inert form of his colleague.

The Autobots nodded to each other. They transformed into their robotic modes and ignoring the police cordon and the shocked stares of the onlookers, they strode toward Tracks.

Aware of a movement outside the bank, J.D. looked out of the window and was greeted with the sight of three giant robots! They were crouched by the side of the Corvette.

"He doesn't look good," one of them said.

"Oh my..." whispered J.D., as panic rose within him. He stumbled backwards, knocking into a table. The bag containing the dynamite crashed to the floor and a ticking came from the time piece...

FIRE!

The Autobots were thrown to the ground by an explosion that completely destroyed the bank's frontage. The rest of the building was engulfed in a ball of flame.

"The hostages – they're still in there!" cried a police officer.

Inferno heard this as he picked himself up off the ground. He shouted to the Autobots, "Take Tracks out of harm's way and then get back here. There are humans trapped in that burning building! We must save them!"

Quickly, Grapple transformed into his vehicle mode and drove close to the building. Using his crane attachment, he began to ferry people from the roof, where they had fled to avoid the flames. Meanwhile, Hoist, still in his robotic form, used his incredible strength to hold up the ceiling of the bank's ground floor, while Inferno, also in robotic form, pulled unconscious victims to safety.

After ten minutes of this frenzied activity, the Autobots had managed to evacuate everyone from the building. Or so they thought. J.D. and Mark were delivered straight into the hands of the police.

"There was a young boy," cried a woman. "He entered the bank after the robbery had started. I can't see him! He must still be in there! Someone's got to go in and rescue him."

INTO THE FLAMES!

"I'll go," yelled Inferno. He entered the flaming building, extinguisher rifle in hand.

Both humans and Autobots stared into the ever-worsening flames. Suddenly, with a terrible crashing noise, the remains of the bank collapsed into a smouldering ruin. Neither Inferno nor Danny could be seen. Long minutes ticked by, and then there was movement from below the glowing ashes. Inferno rose up, burnt wood and plaster falling from his robotic body. Gently cradled in his arms was the still form of Danny.

Hoist and Grapple ran toward their friend.

"Is the boy all right?" Grapple demanded.

"Yes," replied Inferno, "I shielded him from the flames with my own heat resistant body."

He looked down at the funny, pink life form, so different from themselves. A smile appeared on Inferno's face, as the boy stirred in his arms. He was glad he'd been able to save the little thing...

A LESSON FOR TRACKS

The injured were taken to hospital and both Mark and J.D. were carried off by the police. The disabled Tracks was placed on the back of Hoist and the group of Autobots set off back to Oregon.

Back at the Ark, after Tracks had been restored by Hoist and Ratchet, he was debriefed by Optimus Prime. Tracks went through all the events that had led up to the fire.

"Surely if humans behave in the same manner as those two crooks and threaten the lives of fellow-humans," he remarked, "they are as bad as the Decepticons and deserve to be ruled by them?"

"You are wrong, Tracks," Optimus Prime told him firmly. "There is a world of difference between the evil of all Decepticons and the wrong-doings of a number of the humans. And there is something you must never forget: there are also countless honest humans, and it is they we are sworn to protect!"

They were words that Tracks never forgot...

JUMP IT, BLUESTREAK - I'LL COVER YOUR BACK...
YEAH... BUT WHO'LL COVER **YOURS?**
THE LUCK OF THE DAY IS WITH BLUESTREAK...
KROOM SCREEEEE!
BUT UNFORTUNATELY, FOR FUSION IT IS ANOTHER STORY...
OOPS!
NO! NOOOO!
BLUESTREAK CAN DO NOTHING TO AID HIS COMRADE-IN-ARMS... NOTHING BUT SWEAR **REVENGE**!

MEANWHILE, IN A COMMAND POST IN IACON...
GIVE ME YOUR REPORT QUICKLY, I MUST RETURN TO THE BATTLE...

EMIRATE XAARON ON SECURITY CHANNEL ONE, COMMANDER.
AT LAST...
XAARON, THIS HAS GONE TOO FAR...
FEAR NOT, OPTIMUS. TRAACHON IS HANDING OVER FULL CONTROL OF THE ARMY TO YOU - THE FATE OF THE AUTOBOTS IS IN YOUR HANDS NOW.
GOOD LUCK.

AT LAST. NOW I CAN STRIKE POSITIVELY AGAINST THE ADVANCING DECEPTICONS...
HAVE BLUESTREAK AND FUSION REPORTED IN YET?
FUSION DIDN'T MAKE IT...
BUT BLUESTREAK'S BACK - WE'RE UNLOADING THE BOMBS NOW...

AND WHILST OPTIMUS PRIME ASSUMES HIS NEW ROLE OF LEADER OF THE AUTOBOTS, HIS OPPOSITE NUMBER, MEGATRON, SURVEYS THE DAMAGE WROUGHT BY HIS TROOPS' AERIAL BOMBARDMENT.
FINALLY, TOTAL VICTORY IS WITHIN MY GRASP... ONCE IACON HAS FALLEN, THE REMAINING AUTOBOT STRONG-HOLDS WILL BE EASY TO PICK OFF WHEN IT SUITS ME...

...ALL CYBERTRON WILL BE UNDER DECEPTICON RULE... **MY RULE**!

SOUNDWAVE - STATUS REPORT..?
THE DECEPTICON ADVANCE HAS DRIVEN THE AUTOBOTS BACK WITHIN THE OUTER PERIMETER OF THE CENTRAL DOME. THEY WERE ORDERED TO REGROUP A FEW MOMENTS AGO...

PERFECT! ALERT THE STRIKE FORCE - WE ATTACK IACON CENTRAL **IMMEDIATELY**...
NO-ONE CAN STOP US NOW!
HALT! I WILL ALLOW YOU TO GO NC FURTHER!

I AM OPTIMUS PRIME, LEADER OF THE AUTOBOTS! I SUGGEST THAT YOU SURRENDER NOW, MEGATRON...
OR FACE THE CONSEQUENCES!
SURRENDER?
SURRENDER?!
ATTACK!
KILL THEM ALL!
AND SO THE BATTLE IS JOINED...
HOWEVER, IT SOON BECOMES EVIDENT THAT THE AUTOBOTS ARE HEAVILY OUTNUMBERED...AND WILL SOON FALL
UNLESS, OF COURSE, THEY HAVE ONE MORE HAND TO PLAY...
THAT'S IT, OPTIMUS, JUST KEEP THEM THERE A FEW MOMENTS LONGER...
INCREDIBLE TO THINK THAT WE'VE BEEN PLANNING THIS MOMENT FOR WEEKS AND IT HAS, AT LAST, BECOME A REALITY!
WEEKS OF PATIENTLY WEAKENING THIS PARTICULAR PAIR OF EXPRESSWAY SUPPORTS, OF COMMANDO RAIDS - EACH ONE A DESPERATE SEARCH FOR SHATTER BOMBS.

AND ALL WITHOUT THE COUNCIL SUSPECTING WE WERE ACTING WITHOUT THEIR APPROVAL. AND NOW, TO COME TOGETHER SO NEATLY... THE SHATTER BOMBS, THE DECEPTICON ATTACK AND THE COUNCIL RULING...

WE'RE FINISHED HERE.

" IT'S UP TO YOU NOW, OPTIMUS...'
SHRAACK!
THAT WAS TOO CLOSE FOR COMFORT... BUT, NOW THAT GEARS HAS SIGNALLED HE'S READY, IT'LL HAVE TO BE CLOSER STILL...

I MAY BE DEFEATED, MEGATRON...
BUT I'LL TAKE YOU WITH ME!

SOMEHOW, OPTIMUS PRIME...

... I DON'T THINK SO!
KROOM!

UNNGH..! FLEE, AUTOBOTS! CARRY ON THE STRUGGLE FOR ME.

OBEYING THEIR LEADER'S LAST COMMAND, THE AUTOBOTS STAGE A SOMEWHAT PANICKED RETREAT...
HA! I MUST THANK YOU, OPTIMUS PRIME, SEEING YOUR TROOPS FLEE IN ABJECT FEAR HAS ALMOST COMPLETED MY VICTORY...

ONLY ONE TASK REMAINS...
YOU'RE SO RIGHT...

KAABOOOM!

THOUSANDS OF TONS OF METAL CRASH TO THE GROUND - SMASHING AND CRUSHING THE DECEPTICONS TO THE GROUND.
IT SEEMS IMPOSSIBLE THAT ANYONE COULD SURVIVE SUCH A MAELSTROM OF DESTRUCTION...

BUT PERHAPS TODAY IS A DAY FOR MIRACLES...
GOT 'IM!

TOLD YOU MY MAGNETIC POWERS COULD PLUCK HIM OUT OF THERE!
QUICKLY, GET HIM TO THE MED-BAY. WE'LL NEED HIM BACK IN ACTION WHEN THE DECEP--TICONS SEND IN REINFORCEMENTS!

DO YOU RECKON WE'VE FINALLY GOT RID OF MEGATRON?
MUST HAVE. I MEAN...

"NOTHING COULD HAVE SURVIVED THAT!

SCHRAAAK!

I... LIVE! YOUR PLOY HAS FAILED OPTIMUS PRIME!

YOU HAVE WON A BATTLE BUT THE WAR GOES ON... I WILL NOT REST UNTIL I DESTROY YOU UTTERLY!

AND GO ON THE WAR DID... STRETCHING FROM CYBERTRON TO EARTH.
BUT NEVER ONCE DID OPTIMUS PRIME SHIRK THE RESPONSIBILITY THAT HAD BEEN HANDED TO HIM... THE RESPONSIBILITY OF A LEADER!

MATCH THE AUTOBOT ROBOT AND VEHICLE

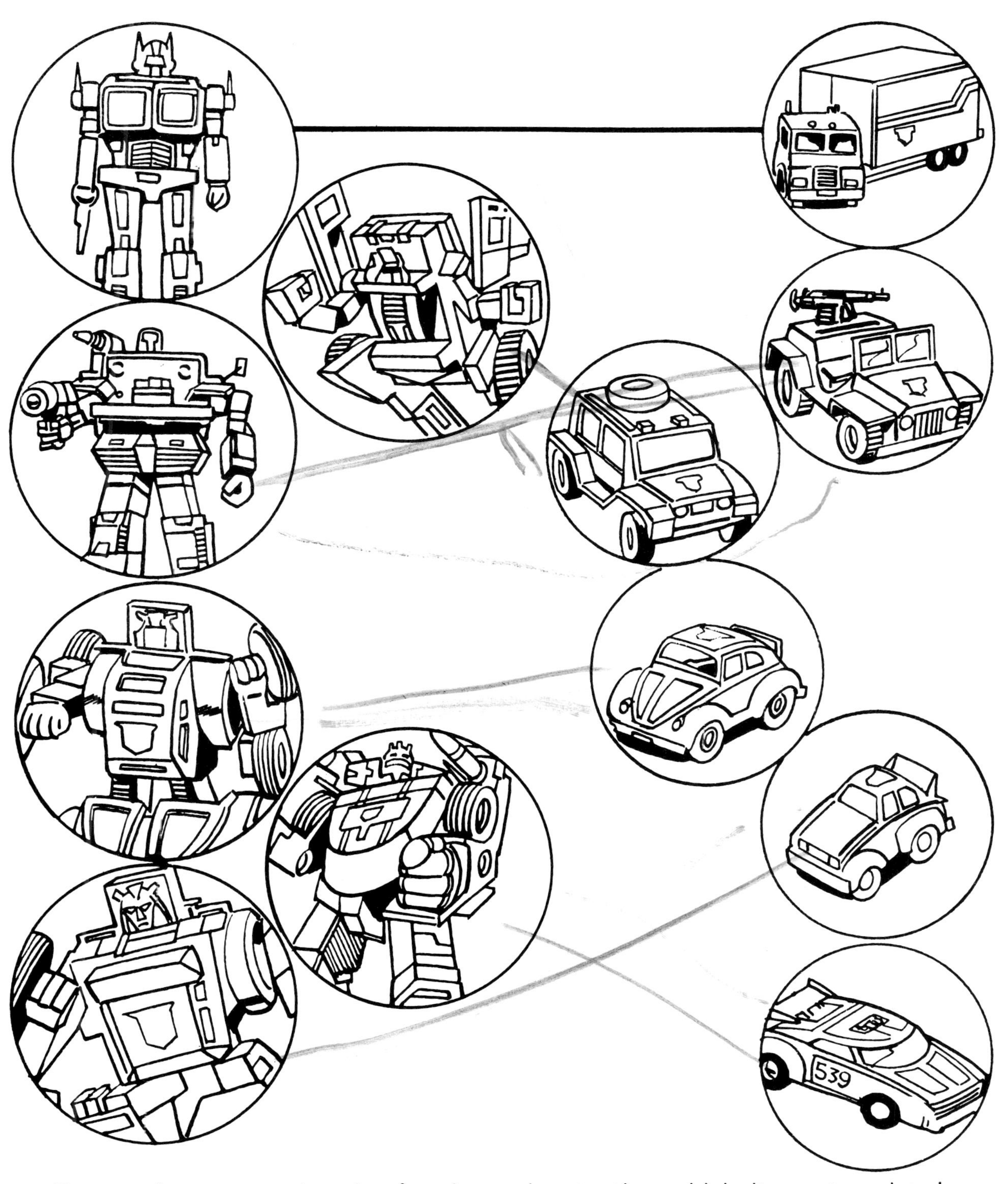

Draw a line connecting the Autobot robot to the vehicle it can turn into!
We did the first one to show you how!

The solution to this puzzle is on page 62.

HEXAGONAL ATTACK ON
In the age-old conflict between the Autobots and the Decepticons, the fighting ebbs backwards and forwards. Play this game with dice and markers; begin at the starting point; throw the dice, then move through the right-numbered side of the hexagon for direction. First to get to the red castle wins!
2 1
3 6
4 5

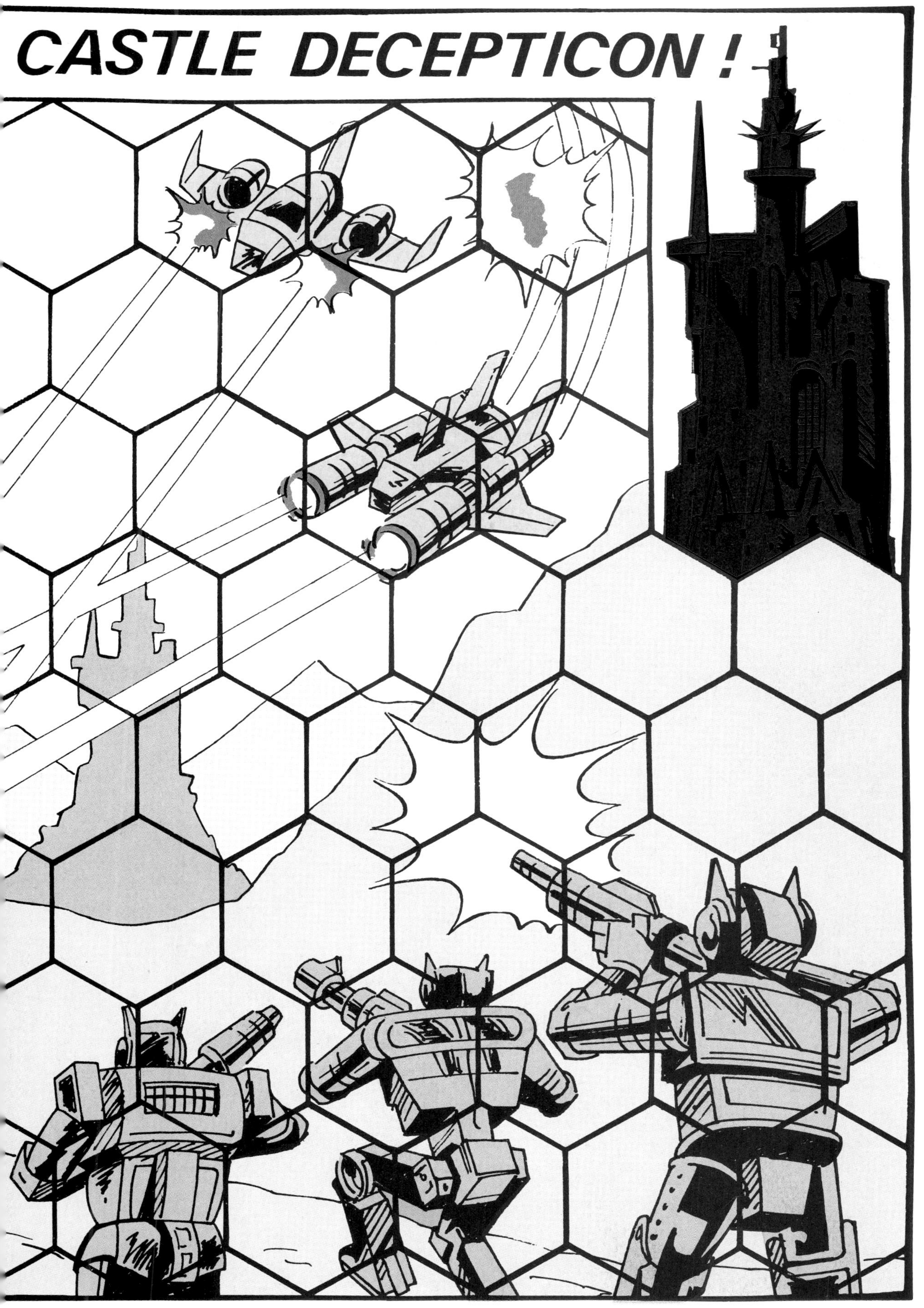
CASTLE DECEPTICON!

HUNTED!

All Bumblebee wanted was to see some action. Soon he would see too much!

Dawn in South America and life returns to the jungle. Jungle beasts, perched on their tree branches, begin to stir. The birds rise and celebrate the day's arrival with a high-pitched melody. Suddenly alien sounds disrupt the scene. . .

Struggling for breath, the man entered the clearing. He'd been running and hiding for days and his dark rimmed eyes showed his exhaustion. Mud caked the lower parts of his legs and his clothes were torn where the undergrowth had snatched at him.

He hardly saw the tree stump that jutted out from the undergrowth and sent him sprawling on the ground. The man clutched his ankle. *It's broken,* he thought. *It's broken! But it can't be, not now, not when he's so close. . .*

He grasped a branch and began to climb to his feet. That was when he saw it. . . from the corner of his eye, a sudden blur of grey through the dense foliage behind him. There was something in the jungle, something cold and hostile!

The air grew still. There was a faint rustling of leaves, then the undergrowth erupted. Out of the darkness it leapt. It seemed to hang frozen in mid air, a creature of unearthly power, a huge metallic panther. . . Ravage!

The Decepticon's savage assault propelled the man back to the ground. In panic, he struck at Ravage's body with the broken branch, dislodging a small sliver of metal. But resistance was futile and the creature's powerful jaws tore the branch from his grasp.

Ravage crouched by the man's frozen body. "You've led me a merry chase, human," he growled. "But it's over now!"

The Decepticon slowly inched forward. . .

LEFT BEHIND

"Prowl? How much longer must we monitor these news broadcasts?" Bumblebee's words echoed throughout the cavernous room that he shared with the Autobots' master strategist.

"Optimus Prime instructed us to look out for Decepticon activity," Prowl snapped, his eyes hardly leaving the grey image that he watched flickering across a large video screen, "and that's what we're going to do until he and the others return to the Ark."

Bumblebee moved away from his comrade, his arms slumped by his sides. It just wasn't fair. The other Autobots were on a mission, a mission that would undoubtedly bring them into conflict with the Decepticons. It was a mission that Bumblebee had been purposely excluded from.

"It's typical," he muttered, just loud enough for Prowl to hear. "Why's it always me that get's the boring tasks? I bet Jazz never. . ."

"Look. . . on the screen!"

Bumblebee hurriedly spun around. On the video screen an unshaven man could be seen standing in the centre of a jungle clearing. Torrential rain battered his frail form and a blanket had been wrapped around his shoulders. A young woman was gently trying to persuade him to enter a nearby Jeep. Prowl remained motionless, completely transfixed by this image. Long minutes passed before he spoke.

"Can't you see it?" he whispered, almost to himself. "On the ground, a small piece of metal."

"Are you all right?" Bumblebee asked. He was beginning to worry about Prowl. Perhaps the pressures he was under had finally taken their toll on his logic circuits.

EVIDENCE!

Ignoring his friend's concern, Prowl continued to stare at the screen. "Quickly, computer," he shouted, "freeze frame! Now, enlarge the picture."

He turned toward his smaller comrade. "According to the commentary I received through this audio link-up," he said, pointing to a heavy cable that connected his chest to the video screen, "that man is Doctor John Butler. He was a member of an expedition team that recently disappeared in South America. The Red Cross found him in the jungle and he's now being treated for shock in a convent hospital."

"That's all very interesting," Bumblebee said, a quizzical expression etched across his robotic features, "but what's it got to do with us?"

The Autobots' tactician pointed fiercely at the computer-enlarged image on the video screen. A small metallic chip was lying in the undergrowth. "That piece of metal is not of Earth design," Prowl exclaimed, "It was manufactured on Cybertron. . . And if my memory circuits are correct, it was once part of Ravage's armoured hide!"

"But that would mean the Decepticons are active in South America."

"It's more than likely. We'd best inform Optimus Prime." Prowl raised his right arm and spoke into a radio transmitter that he'd previously built into his wrist circuits. "Autobot Prowl calling group leader Optimus Prime."

There was no reply. Prowl switched to another frequency. "Prowl calling Optimus Prime." Again nothing. Not even the faintest whisper of a signal. "It's no good," Prowl cried, "something's interfering with the radio transmissions. I'm receiving nothing but static!"

Rage swelled within him and he tore the audio link up from his chest in an uncharacteristic fit of anger. A shower of sparks was sent across the room.

"Hey, watch it!" cried Bumblebee.

Prowl marched toward the room's exit.

"So what do we do now?" Bumblebee shouted after him.

"There's nothing we can do," he replied, "except wait."

"Wait!" Bumblebee chased after the taller Autobot, placing an arm on his friend's shoulder. "The longer we remain inactive, the greater any possible threat becomes. Surely the two of us should go to South America and investigate."

"No," Prowl said, as he turned and looked down at Bumblebee. "Such a move is out of the question. We've no idea of the Decepticons' strength or of Megatron's plans. Logic dictates that we remain here until Optimus returns. He'll decide on an appropriate plan of action."

"Twin Twist and Top Spin are in the Ark," Bumblebee persisted, "I'm sure they'd help us."

"For the final time, Bumblebee. . . No! We are *not* going to South America."

ACTION AT LAST

Prowl had never been in the jungle before. It was a dark and primal place that defied logic. It was not to his liking. *It's utter madness,* he thought. *How did I let myself be talked into coming to South America? Even with the help of the Jumpstarters we'd never be able to defend ourselves against a Decepticon attack.*

He peered through the trees; some yards up a primitive dirt road there was a military checkpoint. Behind a barrier that spanned the road, Prowl could see a number of jeeps and a handful of well-armed troops. He transformed to his vehicular mode and drove back to where the other Autobots were waiting.

"Well?" asked Top Spin, as Prowl approached.

"I'm afraid there's a road block," he replied. "Perhaps we'd best go back to the Ark."

"I haven't come all this way for nothing," Twin Twist shouted. "I say we just don't stop!"

"Yeah," agreed Top Spin.

"Wait!" cried Prowl, but before he could stop them, the two Jumpstarters had reverted to their vehicle modes, forced their way through the undergrowth, and were soon racing toward the road block.

"Come on, Prowl," shouted Bumblebee, changing to his car form, "or we'll be left behind."

The four Autobots sped along the dirt road.

"Out of the way, humans," Twin Twist shouted, crashing through the checkpoint, his diamond tipped drill splintering the barrier into countless fragments.

The troops unslung their machine guns and fired at the driverless vehicles. Spurts of dust and stones exploded from the road, as bullets rebounded off the fleeing Autobots. A group of soldiers leapt into a jeep and gave chase, still firing their machine guns, but as Prowl and Bumblebee raced past them, they saw them swerve to the side of the road and the soldiers watch helplessly as they rounded the next corner.

DANGER AHEAD

The road soon came to an end.

"This is where we enter the jungle again," Prowl said, less than enthusiastically.

Top Spin took the lead, rotating his drill in order to clear a path through the dense foliage. Ten minutes later, the group entered the clearing where John Butler had been found.

Prowl changed to his robot form and

groped about in the undergrowth. "Ah, here it is," he said, uncovering the grey metallic chip. "It's just as I thought. . . this splinter has come from Ravage's body."

"We already know that," Tc p Spin complained. "What we *don't* know is Ravage's current whereabouts!"

"Oh, but we will," Prowl replied, smugly. "The Decepticons emit a chemical into the atmosphere when they burn their fuel and if we're lucky we'll be able to track Ravage by following the trail left by this chemical."

"In which direction does this trail go?" Bumblebee asked.

"Prowl switched on his sensors. "That way," he said, pointing toward the heart of the jungle.

It's no good, thought Bumblebee, *I'll never catch them.*

After hours of following the chemical trail, he had fallen behind his stronger companions. Now he was standing chest-deep in a filthy swamp. Mud threatened to clog his joints and he was convinced that the damp atmosphere was doing untold damage to his delicate circuitry.

A boa constrictor dropped from a tree and coiled itself around Bumblee's neck; it tightened its muscles and the Autobot's visual sensors began to blur!

There was a sound like the crack of thunder, and the creature was suddenly bathed in a burst of electrical energy. It fell into the murky water, stunned.

Bumblebee looked toward the far bank where he could see the other Autobots, Top Spin was holding his electric blaster.

"You ought to be more careful in the future," Prowl said, helping Bumblebee climb out of the swamp.

Reunited, the friends continued to follow the chemical trail. Hours stretched into days as they slowly pushed their way through the unyielding mass of vegetation. Eventually the group came to an abrupt halt. Immediately in front of them the land dipped and fell, forming the sides of a deep valley.

AMAZING SIGHT

The Autobots stared in disbelief. The valley floor had been levelled and

HUFFER'S WORD MAZE

Huffer has hidden a bunch of words in this maze. Here is the list of words. Can you find them? We've circled one for you.

Look for: MIRAGE AUTOBOT RACHET BUMBLEBEE OPTIMUS PRIME EARTH ROBOT HUFFER

E	M	I	R	P	S	U	M	I	T	P	O
A	U	S	X	R	M	T	A	A	L	N	P
R	T	L	M	N	Q	O	W	X	T	T	Z
T	J	K	B	U	M	B	L	E	B	E	E
H	D	J	Z	A	I	O	P	P	E	H	O
Y	T	O	B	O	R	T	C	A	S	C	U
R	E	W	T	A	A	U	E	I	O	A	C
P	O	U	Q	K	G	A	M	W	P	R	C
Z	H	U	F	F	E	R	V	B	A	M	P

cleared of all plant life and now an unearthly structure towered into the jungle sky.

"That building. . ." commented Top Spin. "It's an exact replica of Megatron's fortress on Cybertron."

"Yes," Prowl agreed, intensely studying the valley. "And behind it there appears to be some form of mine shaft!"

"Mine shaft? But what would the Decepticons be digging for?" Bumblebee's question went unanswered as his comrades focused their attention on the valley floor. Megatron and Ravage were leaving the fortress and making their way toward the mine.

Top Spin rose to his full height, his expression was pale and lifeless. . . but his eye circuits blazed with hatred. He motioned as if to speak.

"Quiet!" Bumblebee cried. "If I concentrate I may be able to overhear part of the Decepticons' conversation." The Autobots fell silent, remaining completely motionless as Bumblebee trained his extra-sensitive audio circuits on the distant forms of Megatron and Ravage. Fifteen minutes slowly ticked by and then: "They're mining for rare crystals, as yet undetected by the humans." Bumblebee's words were whispered in a flat, almost ominous tone. "Megatron hopes to imbue these crystals with artificial intelligence and then place them into recently constructed bodies. . . thus creating an army of Decepticon warriors."

Prowl walked over to Bumblebee. "But how is the missing expedition team involved in all of this?" His voice was edged with a little uncertainty. He was used to the other Autobots coming to him for help and advice.

Bumblebee turned around and for a split second Prowl thought he saw a faint grin on the small Autobot's face. . . but then it was gone.

"The expedition team stumbled onto Megatron's mine and were imprisoned," Bumblebee said. "Doctor Butler escaped and Ravage was sent to deal with him. . . obviously he didn't perform this task as well as he thought."

"We must destroy this mine." Twin Twist said as he and Top Spin moved closer to Prowl.

"Agreed," replied the Autobots' strategist, his confidence returning. "But first we contact the Ark for reinforcements."

SOLO ATTACK

As the group continued to debate possible battle tactics, Bumblebee moved away. He transformed stealthily into his vehicle mode and began to trundle down the valley side toward the Decepticon base. From his eavesdropping, he had learned that Megatron intended to use the humans as a labour force in his plan. Action had to be taken immediately, there was no time to wait for aid. Bumblebee was determined to save the humans. He was after all, their last hope.

Ba-Damm! The Autobots' discussion was broken short by an explosion that rocked the jungle.

"Where's Bumblebee?" cried Twin Twist, realization already sinking in. The group stared in unison at the valley floor. Bumblebee was racing toward the fortress. All around him air to ground missiles were detonating, spraying dirt and rubble across his small form. High in the sky, partially obscured by cloud cover, the Decepticon warriors Starscream and Thrust turned and began a second attack dive.

"Bumblebee's no match for those two. We've got to help him!" shouted Top Spin as he and the others scrambled down the side of the valley.

Only yards from Bumblebee, the Autobots came to a dead stop. Panic seemed to creep through their circuits and they were unable to move. Behind them they could hear the sound of an approaching Decepticon fighter. Prowl tried to overcome his inexplicable fear, however his efforts proved fruitless.

The noise from the Decepticon's engines grew louder. . . Then Prowl recognised a familiar sound. The distinctive echo made by the Decepticon known as Dirge. Dirge, whose engines had the uncanny effect of producing fear in anyone who heard them. Martialling all his logic circuits, Prowl fought against his terror and he turned slowly, his automatic rifle in his hand. Dirge was taken by complete surprise as Prowl fired three acid pellets into his armoured frame. Now out of control, the Decepticon spiralled and crashed into the ground.

Released from Dirge's control, the

Jumpstarters rushed to Bumblebee's aid. Meanwhile, Starscream was preparing to make another strafing run, when the two Autobots fired their weapons simultaneously. The Decepticon was struck by a powerful particle beam and rendered non-functional. He fell to the Earth, completely destroying Megatron's mine in a thunderous explosion.

AVALANCHE!

The Autobots re-grouped and were planning their next move, when Thrust flew past them. The full force of his sonic boom struck the valley wall and the Autobots were suddenly buried under an avalanche of chalky rock.

Bumblebee was the first to tunnel his way out of the rubble. With the mine destroyed, the Decepticons were making good their escape and Bumblebee could see a familiar figure leaving the metallic fortress.

"Megatron!" he cried.

The Decepticon leader turned and looked toward the charging Autobot. "I'd advise you not to hinder my escape," he sneered, "especially as I've planted a bomb in my fortress!"

Bumblebee stopped in his tracks. The members of the expedition team were still held captive in the fortress, and Megatron was obviously aware of the Autobots' vow to protect all human life. He had judged correctly. He watched with a sneer as Bumblebee raced into the fortress to save the humans.

Using his extraordinary strength, Bumblebee freed the expedition team, and together they fled Megatron's fortress, just before the bomb exploded, once again shattering the peace of the surrounding jungle.

The small Autobot surveyed the valley floor. His three friends had finally clawed their way from under the chalky rubble, and he was relieved to see that they had only sustained minor damage. He had behaved rashly and he felt a little ashamed. Nevertheless, he had freed the humans, and although Megatron had escaped, there would undoubtedly be other battles with the Decepticon leader.

HOUND'S SCRAMBLED WORD MESSAGE

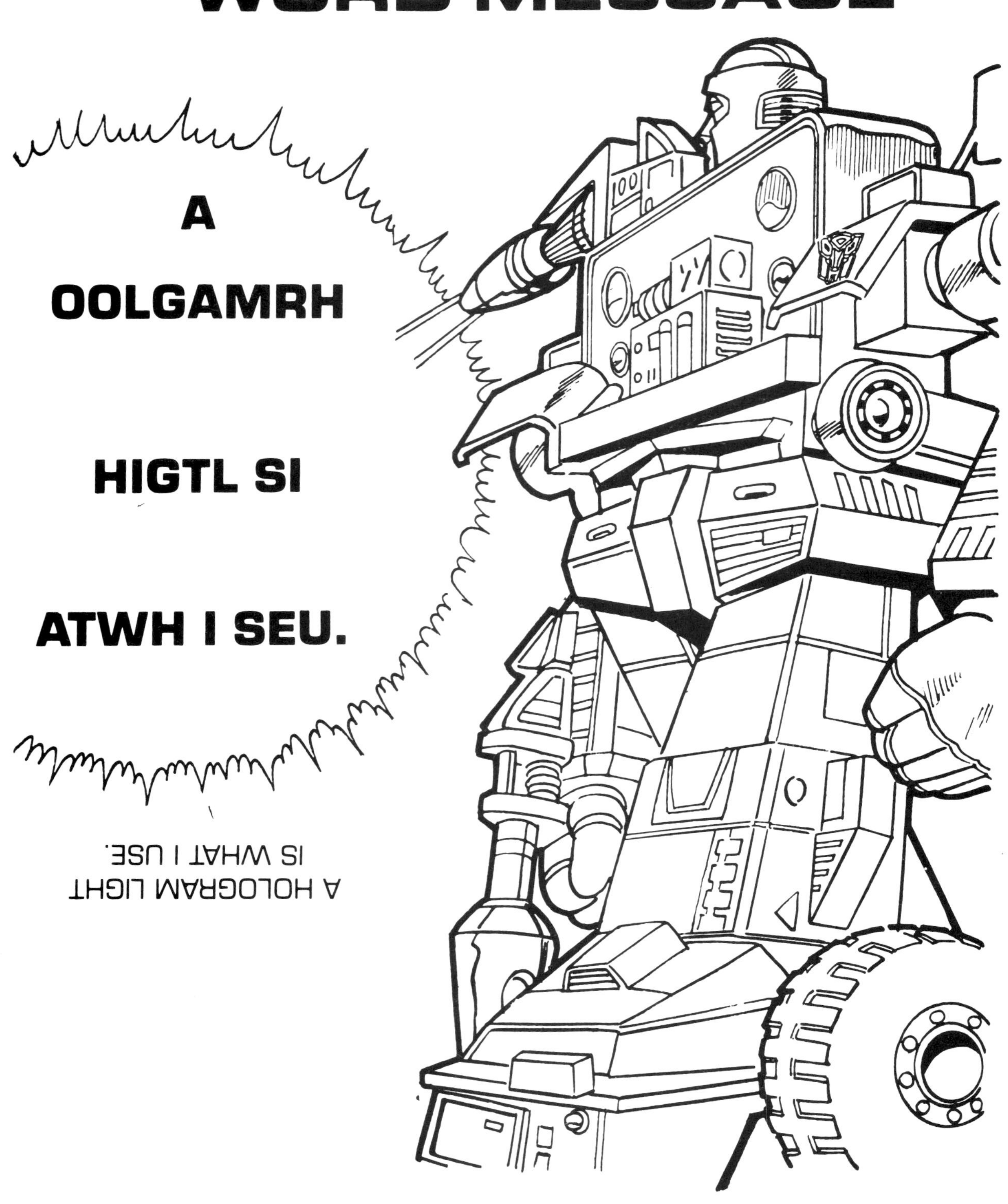

Hound wants you to know the name of his special trick light. But he doesn't want the evil Decepticons to know the name, so he wrote the message in code. Unscramble the words·

CONTINUED FROM PAGE 18

THIS ISN'T GOING WELL--WE CAN'T GO ALL-OUT, FOR FEAR OF HARMING HUMANS...
WE'VE BEEN LUCKY SO FAR...
"BUT I'VE A FEELING IT WON'T LAST!"
PERFECT! PROWL IS UNAWARE THAT SHRAPNEL IS BEHIND HIM...
TIME FOR YOUR SPLINTER GRENADE, I THINK, SHRAPNEL!
KROOM!
WHAT THE-?
GRENADE!

AND, UNLUCKILY FOR PROWL, A GRENADE UNLIKE ANY SEEN BEFORE..!
SHRAAK!
AAARGH!
PROWL!

CURSE YOU!

CURSE YOU ALL!
KERACH!

CURSE ME FOR A FOOL!
PARK

I CAN STILL AID PROWL AND WARPATH WITHOUT ABANDONING MY SEARCH... I'LL JUST BOLSTER THE ARMAMENTS OF MY SCOUT UNIT...

"...AND IT'LL BE READY TO ROLL!"
IT'S NO GOOD! IT'LL TAKE HEAVY-DUTY CUTTING GEAR TO GET IN...

HEURGH!!

WHAT THE-? IT'S OPEN! I WONDER WHAT'S...

RRRMMMM!
INSIDE?

THE MASSIVE SCOUT CAR HURTLES FROM WITHIN THE TRAILER... FAST, STRONG AND DEADLY!
BUT IT IS NO MERE MACHINE, THIS VEHICLE...
VAROOM!

IT IS A LIVING EXTENSION OF OPTIMUS PRIME... IT SHARES HIS THOUGHTS, HIS SUBSTANCE... HIS FEELINGS!
KERAACH!

IT ISN'T GOING TO BE EASY -- SPLITTING UP TO CONCENTRATION... BUT IT LOOKS AS IF I'LL HAVE TO...
IF WE'RE TO WIN THIS NIGHT!

IF I'M RIGHT, MY QUARRY IS IN THIS PARK... BUT I'LL STILL HAVE TO FLUSH HIM OUT...
MUNICIPAL PARK

KRANG!
LET'S TRY THE UNSUBTLE APPROACH!

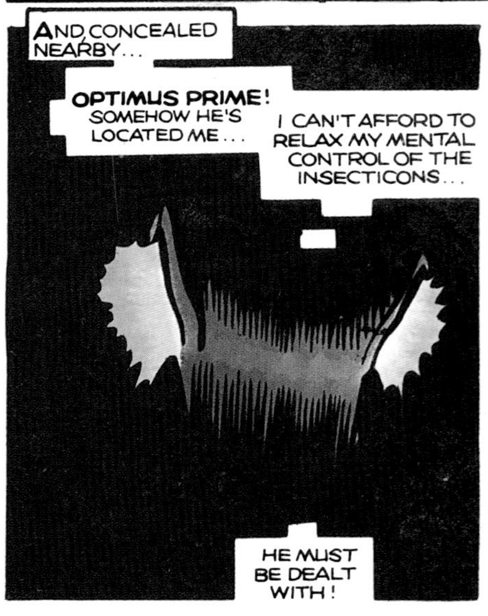
AND, CONCEALED NEARBY...
OPTIMUS PRIME! SOMEHOW HE'S LOCATED ME...
I CAN'T AFFORD TO RELAX MY MENTAL CONTROL OF THE INSECTICONS...
HE MUST BE DEALT WITH!

I'LL HAVE TO DETACH BOMBSHELL FROM THE MAIN BATTLE...
SHRAPNEL AND KICKBACK CAN HANDLE THE REMAINING AUTOBOT...

HOLD STILL, MISCREANTS! JUST LET ME GET ONE CLEAR SHOT IN...

I THINK NOT, AUTOBOT...
IT IS YOUR TIME TO DIEEEEEEEEEEE!

REET!

WHO..?
OPTIMUS! BUT HOW..?
ANSWERS LATER – WE'VE AN INSECTICON TO DEAL WITH FIRST!

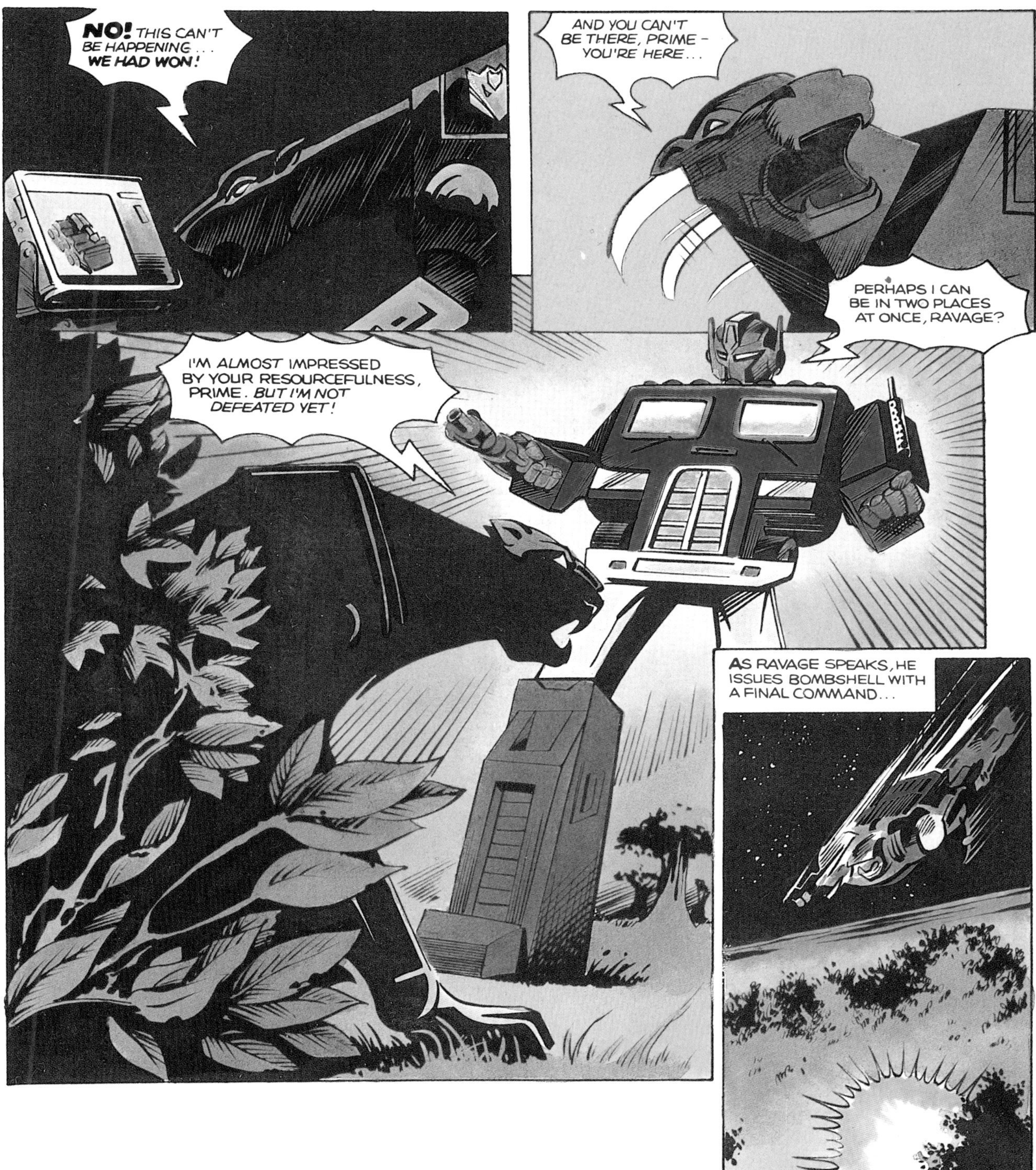
NO! THIS CAN'T BE HAPPENING... WE HAD WON!
AND YOU CAN'T BE THERE, PRIME – YOU'RE HERE...
PERHAPS I CAN BE IN TWO PLACES AT ONCE, RAVAGE?
I'M ALMOST IMPRESSED BY YOUR RESOURCEFULNESS, PRIME. BUT I'M NOT DEFEATED YET!
AS RAVAGE SPEAKS, HE ISSUES BOMBSHELL WITH A FINAL COMMAND...

INJECT OPTIMUS WITH YOUR CEREBRO SHELL - MAKE HIM OUR SLAVE!

RAVAGE'S FINAL MENTAL COMMAND IS SO POWERFUL IT REACHES KICKBACK...
DESTROY OPTIMUS PRIME!

WHO ATTEMPTS TO CARRY IT OUT THE ONLY WAY HE CAN...

AT THAT SAME MOMENT, BOMB-SHELL PREPARES TO INJECT THE SHELL...

THEN FATE INTERVENES...
BATHOOM!
ARRGH!

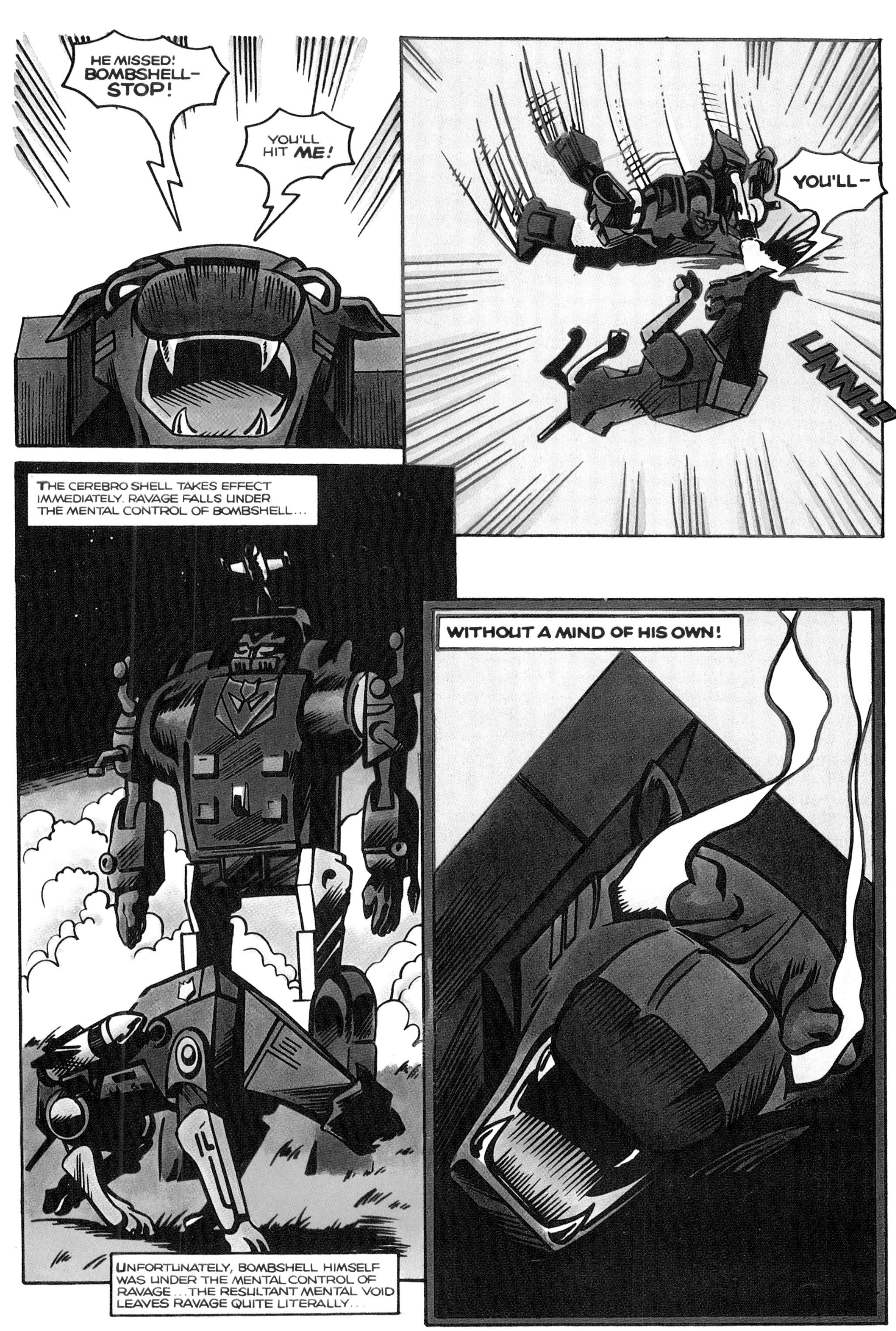
HE MISSED! BOMBSHELL- STOP!
YOU'LL HIT ME!
YOU'LL-
UNNH!
THE CEREBRO SHELL TAKES EFFECT IMMEDIATELY. RAVAGE FALLS UNDER THE MENTAL CONTROL OF BOMBSHELL...
UNFORTUNATELY, BOMBSHELL HIMSELF WAS UNDER THE MENTAL CONTROL OF RAVAGE... THE RESULTANT MENTAL VOID LEAVES RAVAGE QUITE LITERALLY...
WITHOUT A MIND OF HIS OWN!

EPILOGUE:

AS DAWN BROKE OVER WASHINGTON, OPTIMUS PRIME AND WARPATH WERE MANY MILES WEST - HEADING HOME!
DON'T YOU THINK IT'S FUNNY THE WAY THEY JUST LET US GO - SHOULDN'T WE HAVE TRIED TO EXPLAIN..?
NO, THEY'D NEVER HAVE BELIEVED US - I FEAR THAT THE DECEPTICONS HAVE WON TODAY...
WE MAY NEVER BE ABLE TO MAKE PEACE WITH THE HUMANS!

I STILL DON'T SEE WHY WE HAD TO HOLD BACK - IF I'D HAD MY WAY...
WELL YOU DIDN'T SOLDIER. THE ORDERS CAME DIRECT FROM THE PRESIDENT...

WHY DID WE LET THEM GO, SIR?
TRUST, DON, TRUST. THE WAY I SAW IT, THE AUTOBOTS WERE SET UP - MADE TO LOOK BAD -- I GAVE THEM THE CHANCE TO SORT IT OUT THEIR WAY
THEY DID THAT.
I THEN TRUSTED THEM TO COME TO ME TO EXPLAIN. THEY DIDN'T.
I TRUSTED THEM. IT LOOKS LIKE I MADE A MISTAKE...
AND I CAN'T AFFORD TO MAKE SUCH A MISTAKE AGAIN!

RATCHET TO THE RESCUE!

Ratchet must race through the maze and miss all the dangers so he can fix Mirage fast! Show him the right way to go!

ANSWER PAGE

Page 19

Page 26

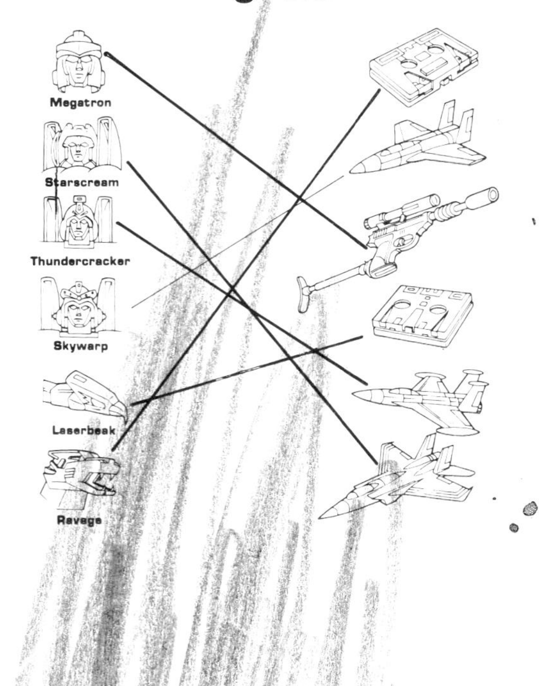

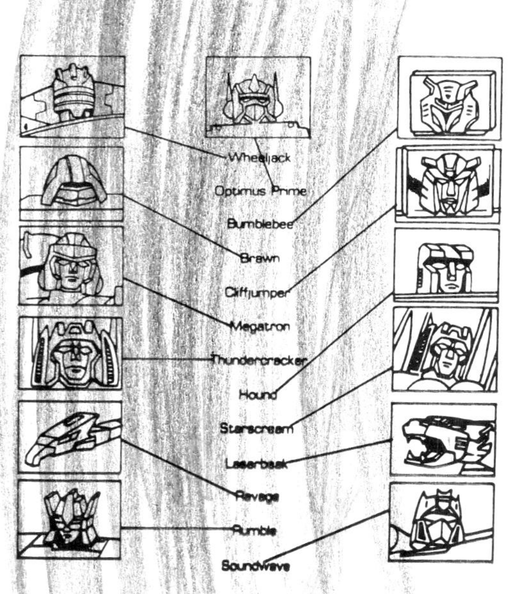

Page 39

Page 41

The fight continues . . . Follow the struggle between the heroic Autobots and the evil Decepticons in their own comic!